The King's Condition

Om
KIDZ
An imprint of Om Books International

The great king of Vijaynagar, Krishna Deva Raya, once had the strangest dream. He dreamt that he was in a magnificent jewelled palace made of precious stones, floating in air. Lit up like a star, the palace glittered with the light of a thousand lamps yet could be hidden from view at a moment's notice, at the whim of the king.

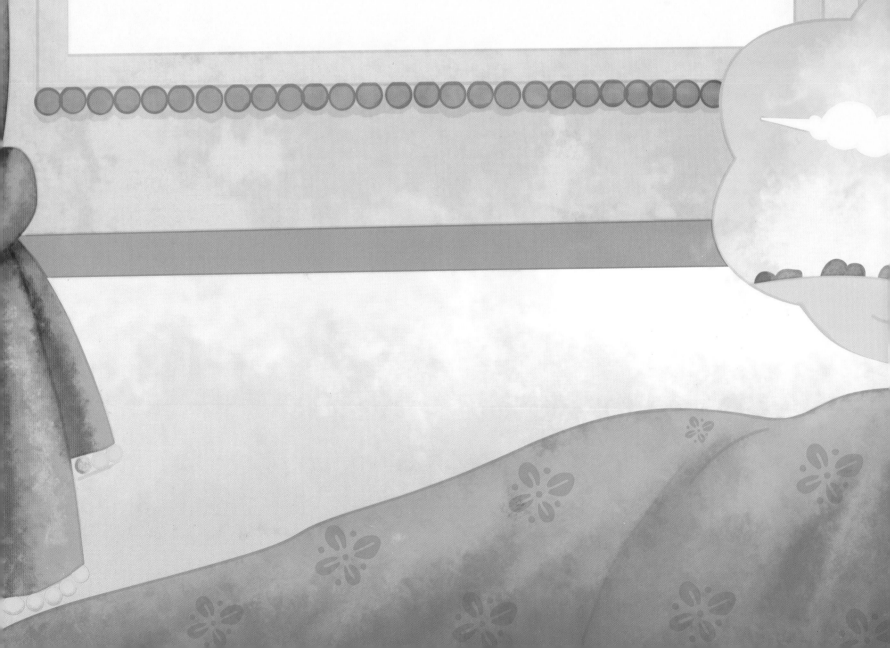

The king woke up from the dream with a great desire to convert it to reality. He announced that he wanted to build the magical palace of his dream.

The courtiers had no objection to this and agreed readily. Excited, the king announced that he would award a sum of a 100,000 gold coins to the architect capable of building his dream palace.

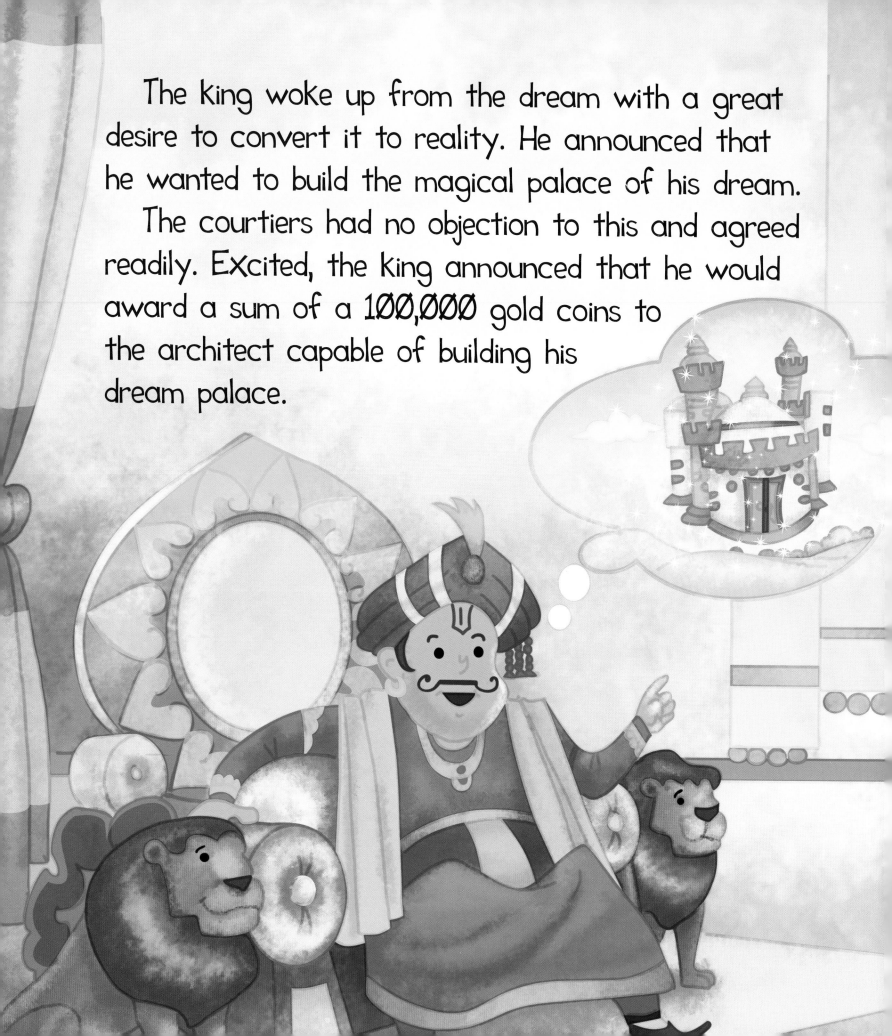

When the courtiers realised that the king was serious about implementing his plan in reality, they grew worried. They knew that nothing would be left of the royal treasury once the palace was built. They wished to warn the king of the consequences of rash decisions but none dared to disobey or defy the king.

A few of the courtiers spoke up bravely about this to the king, but the king became furious and threatened the courtiers with dire consequences if they failed him.

The courtiers were well aware that the king's plan was but a pipe dream. Yet, they were rendered helpless against the power of the king. Worried, they decided to approach Tenali Raman for help. Tenali Raman was the wisest courtier in the King's court

and was also the personal advisor to Krishna Deva Raya, who was very fond of him.

"Tenali, we have tried to save him from this impending disaster, but to no avail. He refuses to listen to the voice of reason and instead threatens us with imprisonment for disloyalty. It is up to you now—you are our only hope.

"Try to talk to him or else we will be in dire straits very soon. The king has announced an ultimatum if we fail to build the palace," pleaded one senior minister.

Tenali promised to do everything in his power. Trusting him to deal with the situation, the courtiers left.

A few days later, a very old man appeared in the court. He had come to meet the king and demanded justice.

The king asked, "Tell me, my good man-what brings you to the court? Tell me your troubles so I can fix them for you, for I am your King."

The old man wailed, "Good Sir, I have been ruined! I have been robbed of all my savings and now I am penniless with nowhere to go."

"Tell me the name of the culprit and I shall have him punished," said the king.

"It is you, my lord," said the man.

"What is the meaning of this? Explain yourself!" shouted the King.

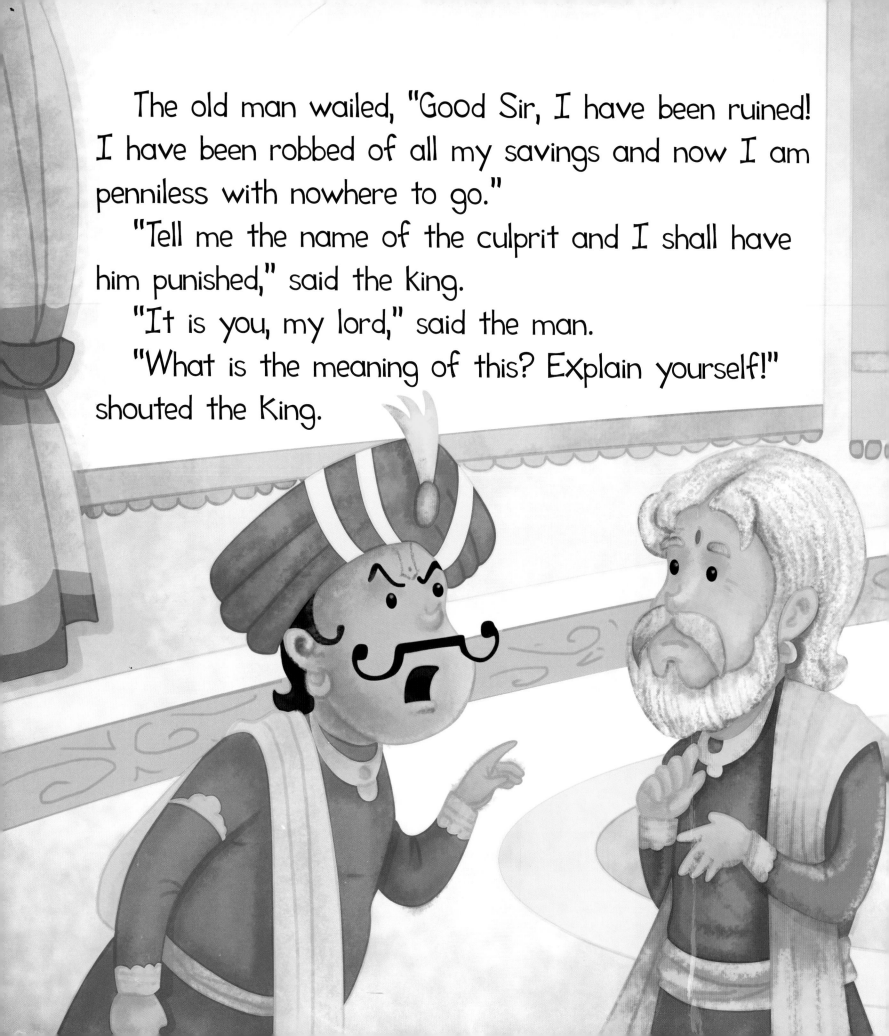

"Your Majesty, last night I dreamt that you invaded my house and robbed me of my entire life's savings, all 5000 gold coins. I demand justice for the crime committed in my dream."

"Are you insane? Dreams are not reality...," began the King, but suddenly realised his folly.

The old man took off his beard and revealed himself to be Tenali Raman, and bowed before the King.

"Your Majesty, now you see?
Dreams can never become reality;
yours is but a pipe dream!"